SIMPLY
PROFESSIONAL

PUBLISHED AND PRODUCED BY
LINDA MEREDITH FOR JEENAVALE LTD

CREDITS:

Published and Produced by
Linda Meredith for Jeenavale Ltd
60 Church Rd, Leyton,
London E10 5JP
Telephone 01-556 5011

Designed and Printed by
Thomson Wright International
London W1

Make-up Linda Meredith
Assistant Jeff Jeffrey
Beauty Photography Jutta Klee
Still Life Photography Donna Trope

Hair Stylist Andrea Moehring
Accessories House of Fraser
Ethnic Jewellery David Joseph
Evening Dress D.X. London

And thanks to Models Rachael,
Varian, Sarah, Mary, Jo Jo, Lianne.

A special thankyou to Jayne Mitchell-
Briggs for her assistance in helping me
to write this book

ISBN 0-9515058-0-7

CONTENTS

Linda Meredith has earned a very particular reputation within the beauty industry. She founded her School of Make-up in 1979 with a commitment to raise professional standards and to pass on her special make-up techniques to as many students as possible. The School is now renowned throughout Europe, the Far East and the USA and Linda travels a great deal at home and abroad in demand as the premier lecturer in the 'art of make-up'.

Linda's first book, '10 Easy Steps to Perfect Make-up', (published 1984) has been a great success. This second book was prompted by two irresistible factors. To begin with, Linda's very close involvement in developing her own range of make-up, 'Linda Meredith Simply Beautiful', to meet her own exacting standards for cosmetics. This brought her into the heart of the technology behind creating cosmetic colours and textures, and led to original and exciting ideas about techniques and the 'creativity' of make-up   new ground was being broken. Secondly, demand throughout the beauty industry for a follow-up to Linda's '10 Easy Steps . . .' was becoming increasingly noisy.

'Simply Professional' brings the reader bang up-to-date on cosmetic textures and techniques for applying them, and the book offers some exciting new concepts. It also includes an 8-page 'Portfolio of Colour' section which helps you to explore the wonders of colour co-ordination using the skills explained in the text.

Linda's aim was to create a bible for professionals and non-professionals alike. This she has accomplished. Nothing is assumed of the reader: the book is written in a straightforward, uncomplicated style with step-by-step guidelines on different techniques. Within its pages you will also find old myths exploded, new and simple ways to achieve beautiful results, and special tips on how to get the best out of some awkward cosmetics.

'Simply Professional' offers a new understanding of cosmetics that will leave you well equipped to perfect your skill and to develop your individual flair!

"Make the cosmetics work for you"

My motto is, "make the cosmetics work for you". Perhaps this is why I have always strived so hard to develop special techniques to overcome the limitations imposed by many of the available cosmetic textures. Another part of my philosophy is 'keep it simple'. Make-up and the art of make-up are subjects that are greatly over-complicated: even the professional can get confused by the conflicting advice and information, and the overwhelming choice of cosmetics. In my view this confusion isn't necessary, and I have set out to take the mystique and science out of cosmetics and their application. The aim is to offer an easy and thorough understanding of an art that we can all benefit from so enormously.

I do claim, unashamedly, that my techniques are the best. My big frustration has always been having to work with other people's cosmetics: textures that just weren't quite right and colour ranges that are far too limiting. This is why, in my innocence, I decided to develop my own make-up range in an attempt to achieve perfection.

Had I any real notion of the complexities involved in the production of cosmetics, never mind the horrors of selecting the right packaging materials, shapes, colours and so on, I might never have taken my first step. But innocence proved to be my friend. I wanted to know everything, and I had very clear ideas about the textures and the colours that I needed to develop.

So, it's been over a year living on the other side of the fence; working with top chemists in the field, and travelling wherever necessary to explore new possibilities — USA, Far East, Germany — to get the results that I wanted.

Perhaps the project that excited me most was the creation of my 'Portfolio of Colour' for Eye-Shadows. The portfolio has a spectrum of glorious colours graduated from light to dark in rows of greys, light blues, dark blues, pinks, browns and so on, which enable you to achieve any look that you ever dreamed of.

I am proud of my 'Simply Beautiful' make-up and will stand by it anywhere in the world (I have to, we're already in the States!). In developing the different products I gained invaluable knowledge and have adapted application techniques where necessary. This experience I now hand on to you along with some new methods and special tips. Above all I keep it simple for I just don't believe in giving you what you don't need be it product or information! Have fun, and enjoy the book.

Linda Meredith

F O U N D

Foundation is one of the most important cosmetics.

It provides the backdrop to all other make-up,

and until you perfect its application you will

never achieve a professional finished look.

ATION

The main purpose of foundation is to 'even out' natural skin tone to give a smooth harmonious effect. It can also be used to achieve a subtle change in skin colour. Foundation is, as well, the best natural concealer for blemishes and general skin problems if applied with a special technique explained later in this section.

When selecting a foundation think only in terms of light, medium and dark in beige tones. If you choose from a vast range of colours you are almost sure to go wrong. Just consider that a good professional needs no more than the basic shades plus, when necessary, a white foundation base which can be mixed to create an ideal colour match.

Tip:– To select a foundation shade use your forehead as a match rather than the back of your hand. It is, after all, the skin tone of your face you are planning to harmonise and colour, not your hand.

Tip:– To change skin colour select your shade very carefully as it needs to be taken on to the neck for a 'total' look. Good blending is particularly important and special attention should be given to the area under the chin.

T E X T U R E S

Foundations are available in Mousse, Liquid, Cream, Solid, and Cake presentations. Liquid and Cream are the most popular for the looks we want to achieve because they create the most natural effect. All Liquid and Cream Foundations are based on a mix of oil and water. Oil provides ease of application and water provides the staying power. The majority of products available contain more oil than water to ensure an easy application but too much oil makes the staying power unreliable (i.e., the make-up starts to 'slide' and so coverage on the skin becomes thinner and can disappear altogether).

Ideally, a foundation should give us six to eight hours of 'stable' cover but in order to guarantee this the balance of oil and water has to be more in favour of the latter. In the 'Simply Beautiful' range the foundations have been finely balanced to give more of the benefits of water (staying power) whilst retaining those of oil (application). They have been further perfected by the development of two under base creams (one of which is a sealer).

Because the formulation of both Liquid and Cream Foundation is similar, the decision about which one to use should have nothing to do with the person's skin type. Liquid is a finer, see-through texture that easily achieves a natural look; Cream is a heavier consistency (roughly double the thickness of liquid) and provides more cover on the skin. *However,* with simple and careful application techniques each can be made to do the job of the other very successfully. The flexibility this provides is very important.

Some people have a strong preference for one or the other texture, and some skins naturally suit liquid or cream. Now, with an innovative method of application, explained later in this section, you can make your preferred foundation do exactly the job you want it to do. Two layers of liquid can provide an excellent smooth cover for problem skin or a heavier night-time look; and a sensitive blending of cream foundation can provide a beautiful, natural day look. The motto is, 'make the cosmetics work for you.'

Mousse is another foundation suitable for normal use. It is very light and has a higher balance of water to oil to achieve staying power. However, because of the high water content it is necessary to apply the product quickly and efficiently to prevent streaking.

Solids, such as Pan Stick, are wax based and are mainly used in specialised make-up such as Stage, TV, and Film. They are also useful in distance work such as that required for Fashion Shows. Pancake is a complete cover that is applied with a damp sponge or Chamois leather to give a matt finish. it does not require powder and so is ideal for body work and for male make-up (some TV Companies use it).

Tinted Gels and Sports Creams give colour but no coverage and are not classified as foundations.

T O O L S

Correct pressure is the 'key' to all make-up application and is especially important when applying foundation. Having the right 'tools' to work with is the first step to turning the 'key'.

There are many applicators which can be used to apply foundation. The right choice is the one that best suits the individual. That is, the 'tool' that is most comfortable to work with and that will therefore help to produce the perfect result.

Certain applicators and textures do, however, work better together. It is well worth experimenting with the different combinations before you commit to anything.

The choice of applicators range from Latex 'Wedges', real Sponges, Chamois leathers, Synthetic Sponges, even your own fingers and last, but not least, a blending ('painting') brush.

A special Foundation Blending Brush with a flat one-inch head of Sable hair is essential. It is used to perfect the finish, after the foundation has been applied to the skin, and is also the only 'tool' that can successfully coat on a *second* layer of foundation. This is because the brush can be used in a very soft painting motion over the skin which smooths out flaws and also allows you to apply additional foundation without affecting the coverage of the first application. This is the only method suitable for this delicate technique. Other 'tools' force too much pressure on to the skin which means that they remove the first layer as you apply the second. So no matter how much foundation you use you would always end up with just one layer.

Most cosmetic brushes are made of Pony hair. But if it is possible, splash out on Sable for all your brushes. Sable brushes rarely lose hair and therefore last 'forever', they also feel beautiful on the skin. Length of handle is important as it affects ease of working and so also quality of application. A six to eight inch length is about the most comfortable and gives a good balance when held in position.

P R E P A R A T I O N

Good preparation is essential to achieve a beautiful, smooth, finished make-up. In the morning the skin should be cleansed preferably with a cleansing bar and a light moisturiser applied. Cleansing and nourishing creams are more beneficial in the evening. If you find your skin is very warm spray your face with water or skin freshener and blot with a tissue. You now have a fresh 'neutral' base on which to start your make-up. It is important to apply foundation as quickly as possible for best results.

SEALERS OR UNDER BASE CREAMS are applied before the foundation as a barrier between the skin's natural problems (oiliness, flakiness) and the make-up. Apart from creating a much smoother finish this preparation protects and enhances the staying power of foundation. However, these products are not always easy to work with. Most sealers are of a liquid formulation and create a dry, tight surface to the skin. This can present problems in applying foundation as it allows no movement, and therefore blending can be extremely difficult particularly with foundations that contain more water than oil.

Through the 'Simply Beautiful' range two very special creams have been developed. The under base cream for dry skin stays 'tacky' long enough for easy blending then dries under the foundation. The other cream acts as a sealer for oily skin; it cleverly combines a cream base for smooth blending and the right level of silicone effect to prevent the skin's oiliness coming through to 'shift' the foundation.

EYEBROWS are last but not least of your preparation routine. Pluck out stray hairs as they will spoil the finish of your eye shadow; generally tidy and balance up if necessary.

APPLICATION

It is worth saying again that pressure is all important whether you use a sponge, brush or your fingers. Too much pressure encourages the skin's problems to show through the make-up resulting in an unattractive, uneven finish. However, the right amount of pressure sensitively applied can work wonders, (see Cream to Liquid to Cream Section for innovative application method).

TO APPLY. Dot foundation on one section of the face only and blend before moving on to the next. If you dot all over some sections may be dry before you get to them, and you will never achieve a smooth finish. Begin with the forehead, then cheek, chin, cheek, nose and eyelids (anti-clockwise direction). Use an Eyeshadow Shading Brush to apply the foundation (more flexible and efficient than your fingers), and blend with your choice of sponge (my preference is a dry Latex wedge).

TO BLEND. Work down the face with a gentle, *gliding* action in the direction of the facial hairs — fade away under the chin. If you work against the facial hairs this will ruffle them and create an uneven finish; it will also take excess foundation into the hair line.

Blend onto the eyelid by gently lifting the eyebrow and working the foundation down towards the lashes. Foundation on eyelids provides a good base for eye make-up and also covers redness, veins and sallowness. However, use modestly or it will cause the eyeshadow to cake. Use foundation (and powder) sparingly also around the eyes, just enough to do the job. Too much will only accentuate wrinkles, lines and 'bags'.

To cover red cheeks and other trouble spots *press* rather than blend the foundation on to the skin as this will cover more effectively. This technique is called *Stippling* and should be used where ever really good coverage may be necessary. A lot of top make-up artists work with a damp sponge but they are very experienced. When learning it is best to use a dry latex wedge, as this will help you to avoid bad streaking.

For a perfect finish use your foundation blending brush in a soft painting motion from left to right only. It will get rid of streaks and even out other imperfections.

CREAM TO LIQUID TO CREAM. I talked earlier about the marvellous flexibility that can be achieved with the right techniques when using either a cream or a liquid foundation. *To make a liquid* give you the look and cover of a cream simply use more of it. 'Paint' on a second layer (or more) with your foundation blending brush using the delicate painting motion. (For a good result with this method you must work very quickly otherwise the foundation will dry and create problems). *To make a cream* foundation give you the look of a liquid use less of it and apply pressure with your applicator to thin out the cover. To finish off use the foundation blending brush to smooth out any flaws. This technique also enables foundation to perform as the perfect concealer.

Simple? Yes it is in theory but it may take some practice to perfect the required sensitivity of touch.

CONCEALERS. There is simply no need for a special concealer. Those that are 'made for the job' are either water-based foundations (for 'stickability') in a small tube with sponge-tipped applicator; or a wax base concealer in the form of a stick. Both are difficult to apply and obvious on the skin. They may conceal the blemish but they do not conceal themselves!

The perfect concealer is, in fact, your own foundation. You now know that most foundations are more oil- than water-based and therefore do not give good coverage for skin problems when applied in the normal way. But using the special application method described in the previous section you can get the level of coverage you need for concealment and still have an even natural finish. Just apply the first layer of your usual foundation, liquid or cream, in the normal way and then 'paint' on extra layers needed with the foundation blending brush. Simple but totally effective. Remember that you cannot apply extra layers with any other 'tool' as the pressure is too great and you will remove the first layer as you blend.

D E R

Most women these days do not use face powder.

This is a great mistake for a few good practical reasons

and also because it gives you a very special, natural finish

when properly applied.

Face powder is an additional aid to 'set' foundation (keep it 'in place') by absorbing excess oil from the foundation and the skin; if you do not use under base creams or sealers it is probably essential. Other plusses are that it also gives staying power to lipstick, and prevents eyeshadow from creasing.

Ideally, a powder should be translucent enough to work on any skin tone — even across the extremes of black and white skin. The ideal demonstrates the fact that the more translucent a powder, the finer it should be, and more able to allow the natural skin tone to glow through.

Tip:— Despite the widespread use of the words translucent and transparent, the majority of cosmetic companies use tints in their powders. Choose the wrong one, or misuse it, and you could end up looking very frosted or a totally different shade.

Tip: Be wary of specially frosted powders. It is very difficult to get an even finish with these, and if you have to apply a second layer your skin can begin to look like a sheet of metal! Better to apply a normal matt powder and add the frost separately.

T E X T U R E S

There are two forms of face powder. One is 'loose' and has to be applied with cotton wool or a powder puff (this should always be your main choice); the other

comes in a solid block and can be applied with a face powder brush or powder puff. This form is ideal for retouching as it is more convenient and less messy to carry.

Block Powder is the lightest and finest of the two textures. It should only be used in conjunction with water based or cake foundation. Loose Powder is essential to set all other foundation textures as it absorbs excess oil from the foundation base and from the skin. Absorption is further helped by 'stippling' (pressing) the loose powder on to the skin.

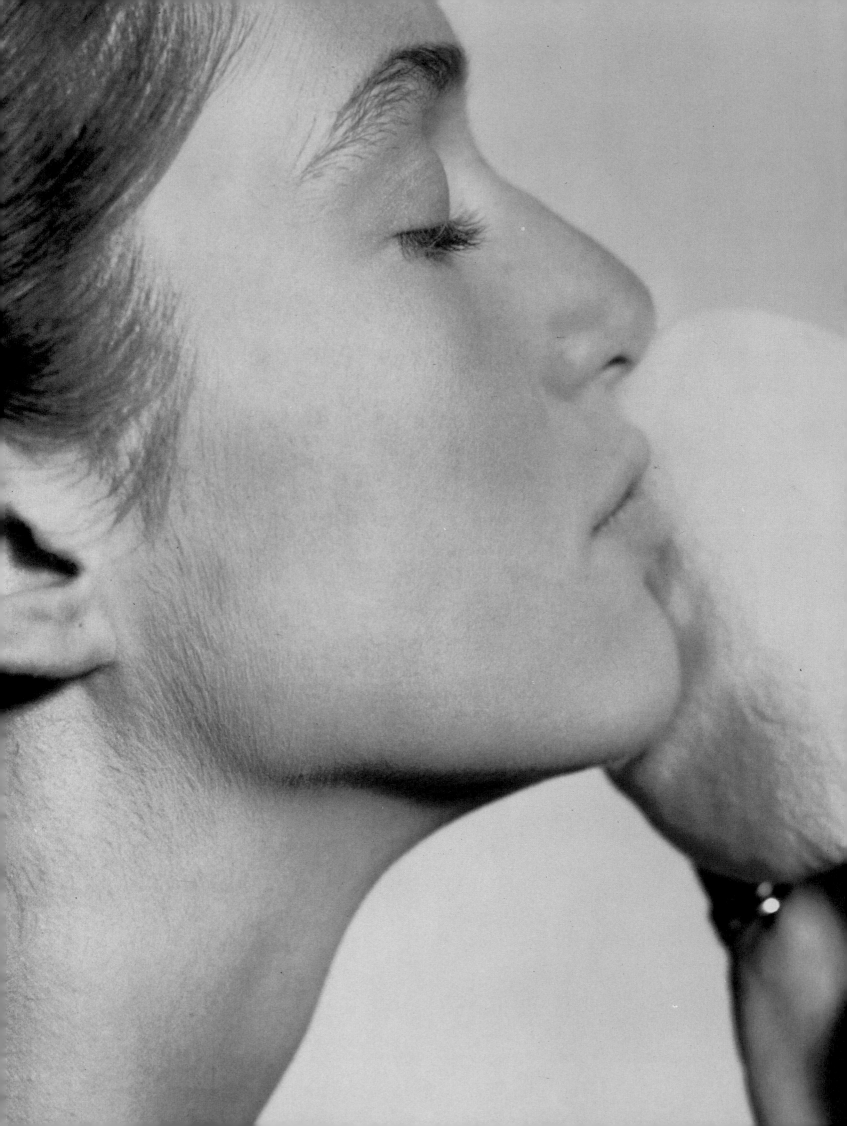

APPLICATION

Apply Block Powder with a Powder Puff or Powder Brush. This is the largest of all the make-up brushes and ensures a fine generous dusting over the entire face. 'Stroke' the block powder on in the direction of the facial hairs (downwards) until skin is dry and silky to touch.

Apply Loose Powder with a Powder Puff or Cotton Wool Pad. 'Stipple' (press) the powder on, small section by small section (upward movements) to achieve a firm setting, good absorption of oil, and to avoid dragging the foundation.

You may be surprised how much powder you need for a satisfactory finish. Test your face with the back of your hand. If skin is 'tacky' to the touch you must apply more powder. A newly powdered face can look a little heavy but once you start moving around, your body generates more heat which produces more oil. At this stage the foundation absorbs any excess powder left on the surface of the skin (if your initial covering was not enough your skin will now start to shine and you should apply more powder).

Eyelids also need a finishing touch of powder. Gently push upwards on your eyebrow to stretch the eyelid. Blend away foundation creases. Dust powder *downwards* only towards the lashes. Otherwise you will 'set' foundation creases and your eyeshadow will also crease.

A blusher is a most flattering cosmetic for any age group.

It adds definition to a face by accentuating the cheekbones,

and selectively used over the skin it gives a warm, healthy glow.

It is useful to apply this colour cosmetic at an early stage, that is after your face powder, as it gives the face balance and will help you when working on your eye-shaping.

Blushers have now replaced the need for contours and highlighters. The right blusher is simply used with a lighter or heavier touch on and under the cheekbones. Unfortunately blushers are easily abused and can do more harm than good. We all know the 'Clown-like' effect that is produced by heavy-handed usage. When applying it think only to give a suggestion of fine cheekbones and a healthy glow. This way it will always be a good and flattering friend, not a resentful enemy.

TEXTURES

There are many different blusher textures available, Mousse, Fluid, Cream, but the most popular and easiest to apply is Cream Powder. This is a fine powder presented in solid form, and with a great variety of colours and shades from which to choose.

APPLICATION

Cream, Fluid and Mousse are usually applied with sponge-tipped applicators or with your fingers, and of course underneath face powder not on top. For added density and staying power cream blush can be applied under the face powder and cream powder blush on top.

A good Blusher Brush is a must to apply a Cream Powder Blush successfully. The head is specially shaped to help you keep to the correct cheekbone area and should be approximately one inch in width. It also gives just a fine dusting and so helps avoid too heavy an application. Blusher technique has been over-complicated in the past but it really is quite simple. The following guidelines apply to all shapes of faces:—

First define the cheekbone area and the angle along which to work. To do this use a thin handled brush and place it across the side of your face. Take as a marker the bulbous piece at the entrance to your ear. Follow an imaginary line down to the corner of your mouth: *call this the cheekline.* Now imagine the central point between the tip of your nose and your top lip, extend the point horizontally running under your cheekbone: *call this the 'base' line.* Your blusher should not drop below this 'base' line

Blusher application should always start at the hair line, just above your ear The hair line can take this colour density; the centre of your face cannot.

To Highlight, apply a light application of blusher 2″ up from the cheekline. To Shade and Contour for shape, apply a heavier application of blusher 1″ up from the same line. Take the blusher no further across to the centre of your face than the outside corner of your eye. Work the blusher on with short, light downward strokes in the direction of the facial hairs, gradually fading away at the correct point. If the end result is blotchy even it out with block face powder.

To add colour to your face extend the blusher along the 2″ line to be in line with the iris of the eye. The use of different depths of blusher (light or dark) can narrow the face or widen it. To reduce the prominence of a high forehead take the blusher up onto the forehead keeping close to the hairline. For a warm, delicate glow add light touches of blusher on chin, nose and forehead.

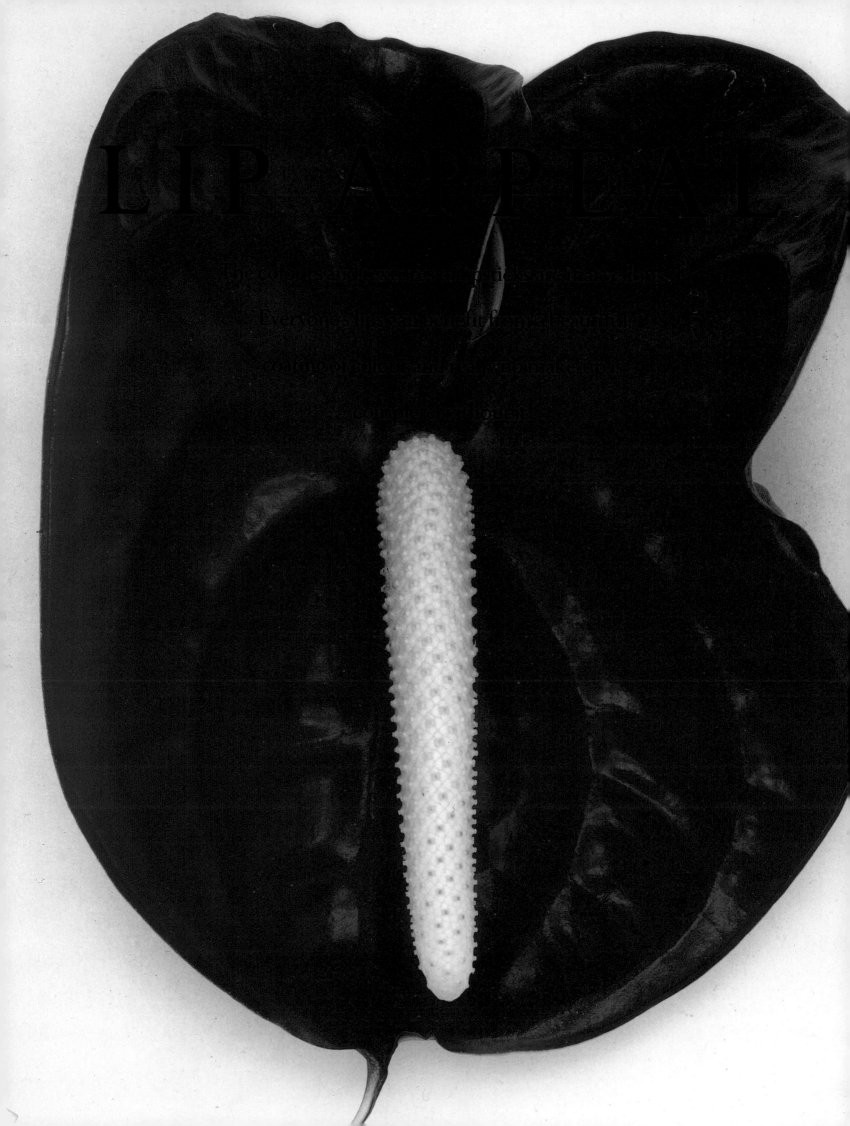

LIP APPEAL

The colour is smooth, the texture sensuous, the gloss mouth-watering.

Everyone's lips can benefit from a beautiful

coating of colour and new easy-to-make tips

play a complementary part.

Lipsticks are available in pots, pencil and stick form. Perhaps because of the great variety to choose from many mistakes are made in selecting lipstick colours. The guidelines, however, are very straightforward. For a classic glamour look your lipstick must always balance your eyes. Therefore dramatic eye treatment must be complemented by dramatic lips; soft eye colours require soft lip colours. It is also important to tone your lipstick with your blusher, and don't forget that make-up is only part of a total look that includes fashion, style and colour, and even hair treatment. Everything should be co-ordinated for a harmonious effect. Avoid at all costs creating a top to toe battlefield out of colour, style and texture!

APPLICATION

For a smooth finish and knife-edge line always use a Lip Brush. It should be a small, flat Sable brush and any straggly hairs must be cut off.

Close lips to give a firm surface. Take plenty of lipstick on to the brush as this makes it easier to achieve a good line. Lay the brush flat against your lips to move evenly along their natural outline. Fill in where necessary. Open your lips in order to colour the corners properly. Always working out from the corner point.

To blot the lipstick place a tissue across both lips and, using the flat of your thumb, press *gently* over your mouth. Too much pressure will take off too much of the lipstick. For extra staying power dust with loose face powder and apply a second coat.

For a glamour finale over-lay lips with gold or silver frost. Alternatively use clear gloss for a tantalising but 'innocent' dewy look.

To accentuate your lips in a more defined way use a fine lip pencil to outline the bow of the top lip and then blend with a lip brush to soften. For a strong contrast or correcting of lipshape, outline the whole of your mouth before you apply the lipstick.

Tip:— Soft, glossy lip colours bleed more easily than harder wax ones. Don't take clear gloss right to the edges of your mouth; it may cause lipstick to run.

Tip:- To stop lip colour bleeding use lip pencil over the entire mouth as a lipstick, and then add gloss.

EYE

DESIGN

Eye cosmetics give colour, shape and definition to

enhance what is possibly our most potent facial asset.

Eye make-up guidelines, like face-shape diagrams, have done much to confuse the willing learner. There are a number of different shading techniques with which to experiment and those described in the following pages in a simple step-by-step guide are suited to all eye shapes. The important thing is to perfect the application and use of products and colours and then have fun experimenting with your own eye designs.

EYEBROWS: As these frame the eyes you should work on them first for they will affect the overall look. Make-up exists to enable us to enhance our natural features not to change them. False eyebrow shaping is definitely not successful; you must work with what you have.

To put colour on to your eyebrows use an Eyebrow Pencil, or a Powdered Shadow which is applied with a short, stiff Angled Brush. An Eyebrow Comb may also be necessary if the hair is quite thick. If using a pencil, colour is gradually and softly applied to the brow with short strokes.

There is a sure technique to avoid heavy-handedness with the pencil. Hold it between your thumb and first finger, very close to its unsharpened end so that it is aimed in a straight line with the point facing directly at the ceiling. In this way you will easily achieve a soft effect as it is impossible to apply too much pressure.

The 'feathering-in' technique is excellent for sparse or very fair eyebrows. Powder and eyebrow brush are best suited to this method. Very gently, and with delicate strokes, apply colour to the hair that is there and at the same time you will mark the skin itself in a very natural way. If your preference is to use the pencil, make sure you apply the correct level of pressure for this delicate technique.

SHADOWING: Cream Powder is a solid eyeshadow and the most popular available. There really is no need to use any other form. Cream powder shadows have staying power, are easy to apply, have a soft smooth look, and come in a myriad of shades and colours. For extra sparkle use eye enhancers which come in the form of loose powder and are applied over the shadow.

To apply and shape shadows you need a good Blending Brush and a Sponge-Tipped Applicator. The latter gives a stronger density of colour, makes it stay on longer and 'holds' the powder more efficiently than a brush (important if you are using dark colours as it avoids unnecessary spillage). For drawing lines an eye-line pencil is the only really successful 'tool'. It gives you the proper control for good true lines and used correctly it does not drag the delicate skin around the eyes. Application techniques for shadows and eye-liner are described in 'Design 1'.

MASCARA: This gives the final balance to the total make-up and can have a very glamourising effect. Today it also comes in a variety of colours.

To apply, look down into your mirror and coat the top side of the top set of lashes. Most of the mascara will deposit here and you will also take off from the lashes any stray eye-shadow. Now look up, and coat the top lashes from underneath. To coat the bottom lashes use the point of the mascara wand.

Tip: — Take excess mascara off the 'wand' with a tissue to avoid clogging lashes. If lashes do become clogged, place a tissue under your eye, close your eye, and comb lashes with an eyebrow brush. To remove specks of mascara from your skin lightly swivel a cotton bud on the spot and remove. Instant spot removal!

D E S I G N 1
(4 colours)

COLOUR 1. This is the lightest of the four colours used in this design. It highlights the browbone and gives a base to the other shadows.

Stretch your eyelid by placing your finger on the eyebrow and gently lifting the skin until you see the eyelashes lift. Apply shadow just below the eyebrow and blend towards the lashes. Cover the entire eyelid area, carefully fading away the colour. Pay special attention to blending away the edges of shadow; they should blend naturally into the skin.

COLOUR 2. The darkest of the eye colours. It is applied with a pencil under the bottom row of lashes and over part of the top eyelid. It is used to accentuate the eye.

Apply a gentle pressure with your finger on the outside corner of the eye. Do not stretch the skin. The aim is to keep the skin tight to get rid of creases so that you can draw a good straight line close to the rim of your eye. Start with the bottom rim. Draw from the outside corner (as this can take an extra concentration of colour) and continue about three-quarters of the way along to fade colour away towards the inner corner of the eye.

Draw along the top lid to a point just beyond the outer edge of the iris of your eye. Develop this line into a wedge so that it is thicker than that on the bottom rim. Blend both pencil lines with a sponge-tipped applicator so that a shadow effect is created.

COLOUR 3. This colour fills an area which extends down the line of the browbone towards the nose and in towards the corner of the eye (see photograph opposite). It contrasts with your fourth colour, is darker than the base colour (No. 1) and lighter than the eye pencil. It has two flattering effects. It gives a soft but greater definition to the nose, making the overall look much sharper; and it also makes the eyes appear larger.

Begin to blend the colour down from your eyebrow following the line of your nose and fill in towards the eye.

COLOUR 4. This is the most important step and it is important that this colour dominates your pale base in order to properly 'stamp' shape and definition. It is darker than colour 3 and slightly lighter than colour 2 (pencil).

COLOUR 1

COLOUR 2

COLOUR 3

COLOUR 4

Before you begin this stage it is a good idea to apply your lipstick to help give a fully balanced face. It will help you to decide on the depth of this final colour.

Apply the shadow on to the top lid over the eyeliner wedge and next to the lashes. Most of the colour will be unloaded at this point. Blend in a downward motion but working up over the pencil area towards the eyebrow. *If* you have no visible socket line blend high enough so that you can see the colour when your eyes are open. *If* you have a large socket area blend colour upwards until you reach the beginning of your browbone, take the colour across the underside of the browbone to blend with the inner point of Colour 3 shadowed area (see photograph). To finish, extend the shadow bringing it around and under the bottom lashes.

The classic shape for all occasions is soft and rounded and should not normally be taken beyond the natural eye socket area. However, if you want a more dramatic look to 'complement' strong colours or a striking outfit you can choose to sweep the colour outwards beyond the socket area.

It is important to pause and check, with the eye open, the shape that you are creating when applying this crucial colour. Build up gradually so that you can judge the effect and see if it is working for you.

WHY THIS TECHNIQUE IS SPECIAL?

With this mix of colours and shading you can create illusions to alter the look of your eyes. You can make small eyes appear larger; or make eyes look wider apart. And with clever use of shading and shaping you can adapt this 'design' to define and enhance your very individual requirements. Well worth lots of practice and experimenting.

D E S I G N 2

(3 or 4 Colours)

If you have no visible socket line then follow this guide to colour 3. *If* you have a large socket area that exposes a lot of browbone then you will need to add colour 4 (this will add the necessary amount of colour to the pale area to add interest and definition).

COLOUR 1. Cover entire eyelid area as described in Design 1. This is again the palest of the colours used but could be slightly darker than that which you would use for Design 1. Using a blusher as a base is effective and convenient.

COLOUR 2. As with all three designs the darkest colour is used here to define and accentuate your eyes. However, for Design 2 you draw the pencil line as close to the lashes as possible around the entire rim of your eye to give a complete outline (blend with a sponge tipped applicator if necessary).

COLOUR 3. Apply a dark eye-shadow over the entire socket line area extending it around and under the bottom lashes.

COLOUR 4. Take a lighter colour than 3 and blend it all around the top edge of the shape that you have just made (check with eyes open).

D E S I G N 3

(3 or 4 Colours)

As with Design 2 you will need the fourth colour only if you have a large socket area.

COLOUR 1. Cover entire eyelid area with a base colour or blusher as for Design 2.

COLOUR 2. Apply eyeliner pencil as for Design 1 (that is three quarters of the way along the bottom rim towards the inner corner of the eye and develop a wedge shape on the top rim). Blend with a sponge tipped applicator.

COLOUR 3. As with Colour 4 in Design 1 apply the shadow onto the top lid over the eyeliner wedge blending down but working the colour up over the pencil towards the browbone. Extend the colour around and under the bottom lashes (see photo opposite).

COLOUR 4. For a large socket area take a fourth colour, a shade lighter, and blend it around the first shape taking it higher onto the browbone (check with the eye open).

All eye designs photographed in the book are taken from one of these three techniques.

PORTFOLIO OF COLOUR

Colour co-ordination is still

regarded by many people as

a 'talent', yet really the basics

are very easily learned.

Some people believe that colour is the key to success in fashion. They may be right. The greatest outfit can look dreadful if produced in certain colours; or worn by someone with incompatible skin colouring; or badly colour schemed with lips & eyeshadow.

There are 'families' of colours that are always harmonious and those that always clash. Some people who do have a special talent or 'knack' can cleverly put together clashing colours and make it work, but it is not necessary to take the risk. You can produce beautiful or exciting colour effects by keeping to the normal rules

In make-up we talk in terms of 'Natural' colours which comprise all the earth and autumnal shades; and the 'Synthetic' colours which comprise all the rest, i.e., blues, mauves, pinks, lilacs, etc. The only colours that repeat in both categories are white and black, although there are subtle variations on a theme such as 'bluey greens' (blue being synthetic; and green classified as natural). There is also a special group of colours, made up of light and dark shades of brown, that are used in eye make-up to create what we call a 'Neutral' look. Keep to one category or the other for a complete make-up and you can't go wrong.

The aim is to present an image of balance and harmony from top to toe. An outfit of Synthetic or Natural colours requires a choice of make-up from the same colour category. The exception is with the use of a neutral make-up; this tones with everything and allows you to wear any outfit with confidence.

Have courage and have fun experimenting with the different looks and moods that colour can create.

Why Synthetic...

...to be cool, calm and collected.

Why Natural...

...to be soft and sensual.

Why Neutral...

...to be whatever you feel.

MAKE-UP INTO THE NIGHT

T he truth is that there *is* no difference between a night and a day make-up. Not unless you want there to be.

Night time 'settings' and moods do give us the licence to be more adventurous — even dramatic. But this can only be effective if you feel comfortable with your new persona *and* if it follows the classic rules (i.e. both your costume and make-up must be balanced in style and colour). Many people prefer to keep to the make-up style that they use everyday — perhaps with just an increase in colour density.

So say goodbye to make-up schizophrenia and enjoy being comfortably you from morning right through the witching hour.

BLACK OR WHITE
What's the difference?

Don't panic! Black skins are not the problem that they are so often made out to be. Yes, ideally use special cosmetics for black skin as these already contain strong pigment that show to perfection on very dark skin. But a beautiful and effective make-up using 'white' cosmetics is easy to achieve simply by choosing colours that are strong enough for contrast. Techniques and textures for application follow the same classic guidelines already described. So where is the mystery to that!

MAKE-UP THROUGH THE LENS

The scrutinising quality of the camera lens, and the high profile of the end product, demands that make-up in photographic work is flawless. Application techniques used are the same as those that have already been described in this book and truly perfected by the photographic make-up artist. He or she will also have the experience to counteract the effects of the full glare of photographic lights and adapt the make-up (e.g. density of colour and coverage) to achieve the required look.

THAT
SPECIAL
DAY

There are some dazzling ethnic wedding make-ups throughout the world but for our classic Bride there is really only one look. Her use of colours can be chosen from any of the three colour categories of natural, neutral or synthetic, but must be delicately applied to be in harmony with the pale, gentle fashion colours that form the backdrop to most Weddings.

SIMPLY BEAUTIFUL

The 'Linda Meredith Simply Beautiful' make-up range is unique in being the first glamour orientated cosmetics to be developed specially for the professional. As such, it is the most critically thought-out and comprehensive range of cosmetics available. But it is also simple. For instance, there are 3 foundations only, in shades from light to dark with a white mix for a 100% colour match. As Linda says, "I don't believe in giving you what you don't need".

There is, indeed, much over-kill in the business but one area that Linda always found very limiting was the choice of eye shadow colours. This is why her 'Portfolio of Colours', evolved with such painstaking care, is such a joy to her. The spectrum of glorious colours in rows of greys, pinks, browns, light blues, dark blues and so on, offers almost unlimited choice. And she sincerely hopes they will provide a colour revolution for many, many people.

Thank you readers,
and thank you to my mother
the main influence on fashion
and colour in my life.

Linda Meredith